The Pianist's Collection

Book One

Selected & Edited by
Alan Ridout

Kevin Mayhew

We hope you enjoy *The Pianist's Collection Book 1*.
Further copies of this and the other books in the series are available
from your local music shop.

In case of difficulty, please contact the publisher direct:

The Sales Department
KEVIN MAYHEW LTD
Rattlesden
Bury St Edmunds
Suffolk IP30 0SZ

Phone 0449 737978
Fax 0449 737834

Front Cover: *The Cornfield* by John Constable (1776-1837).
Reproduced by courtesy of the Trustees, The National Gallery, London.
Cover designed by Juliette Clarke and Graham Johnstone.

First published in Great Britain in 1992 by Kevin Mayhew Ltd.

ISBN 0 86209 250 7

All or part of these pieces have been edited by
Alan Ridout and are the copyright of Kevin Mayhew Ltd.

Series Music Editor: Anthea Smith.

Printed and bound in Great Britain.

Contents

ALAN RIDOUT (b. 1934), who selected and edited the music in this book, is one of England's most prolific composers, producing a steady stream of works in most forms: symphonies, operas, ballet music, chamber music, song cycles and church music.

He studied with Gordon Jacob and Herbert Howells at the Royal College of Music and later with Peter Racine Fricker, Michael Tippet, and the Dutch composer Henk Badings. He has taught at four universities, including Oxford and Cambridge, and for over twenty years was also a Professor at the Royal College of Music.

WALTZ IN E FLAT

Isaac Albéniz (1860-1909)

PRELUDE IN E MINOR

Alexander Scriabin (1872-1915)

PASTORALE

Felix Mendelssohn (1809-1847)

11

HUMORESKE

Carl Nielsen (1865-1931)

HEART'S EASE

Frank Bridge (1879-1941)

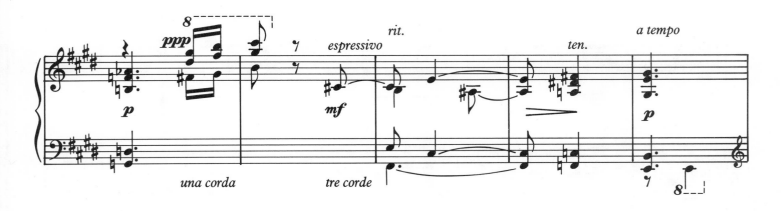

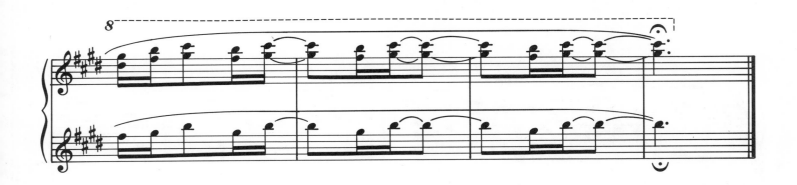

MY HOMELAND

Edvard Grieg (1843-1907)

PRELUDE IN C MINOR

Frédéric Chopin (1810-1849)

GNOSSIENNE III

Erik Satie (1866-1925)

Lent

(Guide yourself with care)*

(Arm yourself with

clear-sightedness)

* Satie's whimsical instructions are included in translation for the
sake of completeness. They are, of course, a joke,
and from a practical standpoint meaningless.

22

WALTZ IN B MINOR

Johannes Brahms (1833-1897)

CEBELL

Henry Purcell (1659-1695)

RONDO from Sonata K. 545

Wolfgang Amadeus Mozart (1756-1791)

ADAGIO from Sonata Op. 13

Ludwig van Beethoven (1770-1827)

ROMANCE

Felix Mendelssohn (1809-1847)

FOLK TUNE

Carl Nielsen (1865-1931)

TWO-PART INVENTION No. 1

Johann Sebastian Bach (1685-1750)

41

FIRST LOSS

Robert Schumann (1810-1856)

DREAM DANCE No. 1

Samuel Coleridge-Taylor (1875-1912)